Winter Ice

'ea'

weather

spread

tread

head

ready

steady

breath

heavy

The weather was very cold in January. There was snow all over the ground and ice all over the pond.

Kevin and Lotty went to the pond to slide on the ice. Kevin slid along with his legs spread out. He loved it.

Then Lotty had a turn on the ice. Her legs spread

out so much that she went round and round in a

spin.

Wellington went to the pond too. He tried to tread on the ice, but he fell head over heels and he landed back in the snow.

Kevin and Lotty wanted to slide across the ice together. They lined up at the edge. 'Ready, steady, go,' barked Wellington.

Kevin and Lotty slid along the ice. Oh no! The ice cracked. Kevin fell in the water. His head went under the ice.

Splash! Lotty fell in after him. The two dogs went under the water. They came up for a breath of air together.

They tried to climb back onto the ice, but it was impossible. They sank back down into the freezing water.

Then Wellington jumped onto the ice with a
heavy thud. It cracked. Luckily, Wellington was
a strong dog. He swam to meet Kevin and Lotty.

He rescued them from the freezing water. They were very cold, but glad to be alive. They did not tread on icy ponds again.

Vowels:

ai/ay/a-e:	again came
ee:	heels freezing meet
ie/i-e/i:	tried slide lined alive ice climb
ow/o:	snow cold over so go no oh
oo/ue:	too rescued
ow/ou:	down out ground round
ar:	barked
er:	over together under after water
ur:	turn
air:	air
ea:	weather spread tread head ready steady breath heavy
soft g:	edge
soft c:	ice icy
-y:	very Lotty January

Verbs:

-ed verbs:	loved tried lined rescued barked cracked jumped landed wanted
Others:	was went slid had came sank were did swam fell

Exceptions: there water they two